DISNEY
PRINCESS
CAN YOU
SPOT IT?

AUTUMN PUBLISHING

DISNEY PRINCESS

The Disney Princesses are on an enchanted search-and-find adventure and they need your help!

Use your searching skills to spot the objects and characters hidden on every page.

Then, once you've found them all, go back through the book to complete the bonus activities and break the secret code!

Cup Clutter

The Dwarfs' cottage is a mess! Help Snow White clean up by finding **4 apples** and **6 strawberries** in this pile of dirty cups.

Rapunzel

Creative and inquisitive, Rapunzel's fearless nature means she will stop at nothing to achieve her dreams. Having spent her whole life trapped in a tower, Rapunzel is still learning about the world around her.

Pascal is a chameleon and Rapunzel's pet and best friend! He also spent years living under Mother Gothel's strict rules.

Maximus is the palace horse for the Royal Guard of Corona. A brave and loyal subject, Max helps Rapunzel to find her way back to her parents, the King and Queen.

Flynn Rider takes Rapunzel to see the lanterns on her birthday. He falls in love with her and changes his ways, leaving his thieving past behind.

Pascal is hiding! Can you find him?

Bad Hair Day

Rapunzel has got her hair in a tangle! Can you help her to find 5 paint brushes and 10 orange flowers on these pages?

Fan Finds

Look closely to see if you can help Mulan spot 8 dragon cannons and 5 fireworks amongst the colourful fans.

Where is Cri-Kee hiding?

CC

Moana

Courageous Moana is passionate about looking after her community, and honouring the traditions of her ancestors. After travelling across the ocean to restore the heart of Te Fiti, Moana realised her destiny as the next great voyager.

Moana's father is the Chief of Motunui, while her grandmother, Gramma Tala, shares Moana's love for the ocean.

Pua is Moana's pet pig and best friend. Heihei is a rooster who accidentally ends up accompanying Moana on her journey!

Maui is the boisterous demigod with a magical fish hook. He and Moana worked together to lift a terrible curse.

Coconut Confusion

The Kakamora are attacking Moana and Maui! Find 11 fish hooks and 6 coconuts as fast as you can!

Heihei is hidden somewhere in the chaos.

CC

Library Look Out

The library at the castle is very busy! Look closely amongst the books and see if you can find **8 letters** and **5 enchanted servants!**

To write her letters,
Belle needs a quill.
Can you find it?

Mulan

Loyal and brave Mulan took her father's place in the army despite the dangers. Using her intelligence and creativity, Mulan was able to outsmart the Huns and bring honour to her family in her own way.

General Shang Li led the Chinese Army against the evil Shan Yu. Shang also fell in love with Mulan.

The Fa family horse, Khan, is very loyal to Mulan. He accompanies her into battle.

Mushu, the impulsive Chinese dragon, and Cri-Kee, a supposedly lucky cricket, are Mulan's sidekicks when she goes to fight against the Huns.

Lovely Lanterns

The Imperial City is celebrating victory over the Huns! Can you find **5 umbrellas and 9 kites** hidden amongst the lanterns?

Mushu is hiding somewhere, too! Can you spot him?

Cushion Chaos

In amongst this huge pile of cushions are 6 pottery pieces and 8 toys. Look closely and see if you can spot them!

Can you find the lamp hidden on these pages?

Ariel

Ariel, a curious and free-spirited mermaid princess, always dreamed about the human world. Having overthrown the evil sea witch, Ursula, Ariel now lives happily on land with her husband, Prince Eric.

Ariel's best friend, Flounder, is a lovable fish who enjoys adventure, despite being a bit of a scaredy-fish!

Eric is a young prince who falls in love with Ariel when she rescues him after he's thrown overboard during a storm at sea.

King Triton, also known as the Sea King, initially disapproves of Ariel's dreams to be human. However, when he sees how happy his daughter is with Eric, King Triton gives Ariel his blessing.

Under the Sea

Ariel loves to swim near to the coral. Can you help her find 8 seahorses, 3 jelly fish and 1 squid?

Can you find Flounder hiding in the coral?

Sew Much To Do!

Cinderella needs to make a new dress for the royal ball. Help her find **9 bows and 6 buttons** on these pages.

Can you find the thimble hiding amongst the wool?

Belle

Clever and strong-willed, Belle will stand up for herself and others no matter what. Belle was always considered an outsider in her town, and this has taught her to look past what is on the surface, and see the best in people.

When the Enchantress cast a spell on the Beast's castle, all the servants who lived there were turned into enchanted objects.

Belle loves to read about places beyond the provincial town she lives in with her father, Maurice.

At first the Beast was angry and stubborn, but as he got to know Belle, he became gentle and kind.

Plate Pile

There's so much washing up to do at the castle! Help Belle to find **9 items of cutlery** and **6 plates of jelly** on these pages.

Can you find the cake?

Merida Mix-up

Merida's shields are in a muddle! Can you find **10 bear statues** hidden amongst the jumble?

Can you find **The Stone Medallion**?

Pocahontas

Free-spirited Pocahontas has a deep connection with nature, and protects the earth and animals around her. A voice of reason and peace, Pocahontas stopped two colliding cultures from going to war with each other.

Pocahontas' father, Powhatan, is the chief of the tribe and a great leader to his people. He's also a well-respected and powerful warrior.

Pocahontas teaches John Smith about her culture, and he is able to see the wisdom of her people.

Meeko and Flit are Pocahontas' animal friends. They are very loyal and always want the best for Pocahontas.

Sunflower Search

Look closely and see if you can find 12 corn cobs and 5 butterflies somewhere in the sunflower field.

Now see if you can find Meeko!

Shell Scramble

Ariel and Flounder are exploring! Can you find 11 forks and 6 items from the human world that Ariel has collected?

Where is Sebastian hiding?

Cinderella

While working as a servant for her stepmother and stepsisters, Cinderella never gave up on her dreams coming true. Now married to Prince Charming, Cinderella is a kind and compassionate princess.

The Glass Slipper was created with magic by the Fairy Godmother for Cinderella to wear to the royal ball.

The Fairy Godmother is gentle, caring and does everything she can to help Cinderella.

As a servant, Cinderella's only friends were the animals, especially the mice, Jaq and Gus.

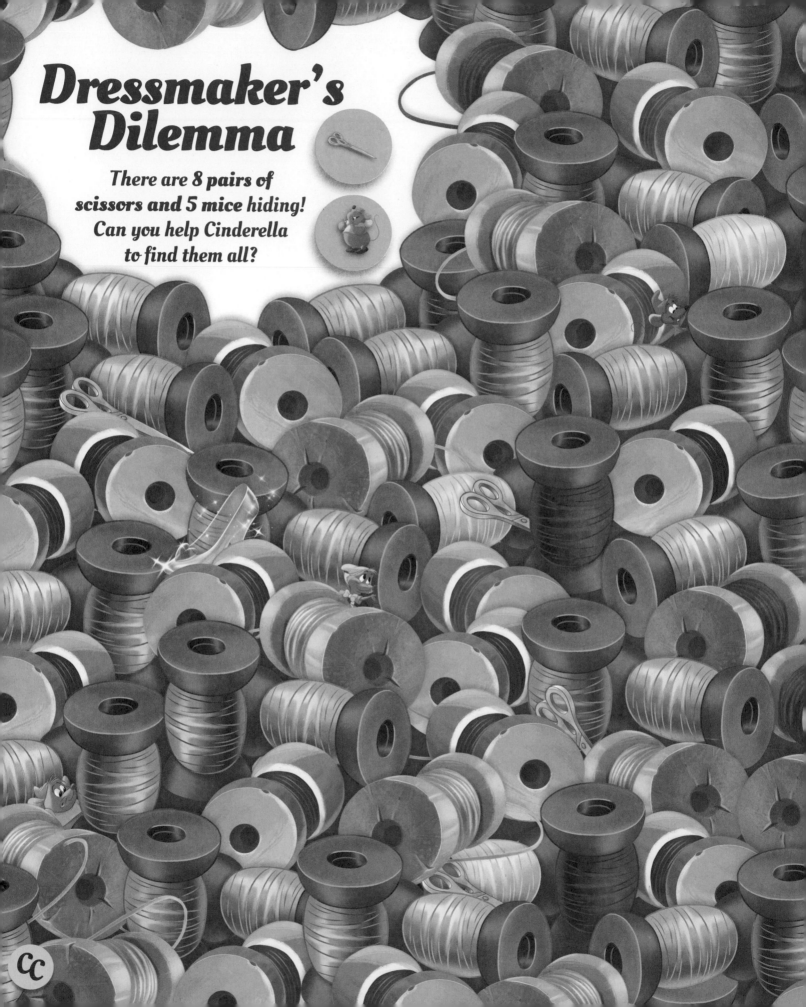

Dressmaker's Dilemma

There are 8 pairs of scissors and 5 mice hiding! Can you help Cinderella to find them all?

Where is the Glass Slipper on these pages?

Jasmine

Independent and compassionate, Jasmine is the Princess of Agrabah. Although she wanted to do right for the people of her kingdom, Jasmine felt trapped and longed for a life outside the palace walls.

The Sultan of Agrabah is Jasmine's father and cares deeply for his kingdom and all of the people within it.

Street rat Aladdin's world is turned upside down when he finds himself in possession of the magic lamp. Aladdin then sets out to defeat Jafar and win Jasmine's heart.

The Genie is one of the most powerful beings in the universe. Having been confined to the lamp for thousands of years, Genie loves to entertain his masters.

Genie Jumble

The Genie has multiplied! Can you find 8 golden gems and 5 bags of gold on these pages?

Now see if you can find Abu!

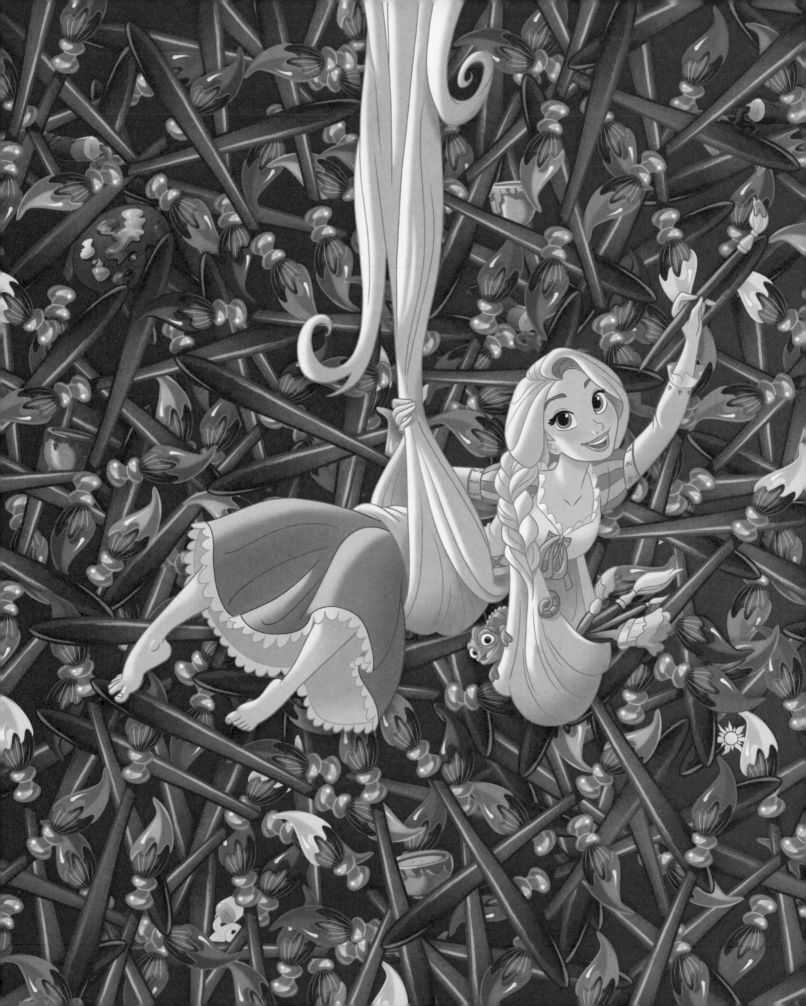

Creative Clutter

Rapunzel is busy painting her next work of art! Can you find 8 tubes of paint and 6 paint pots amongst the paint brushes?

Now see if you can spot the palette!

Aurora

Cursed as a baby by the evil Maleficent, Aurora was raised deep in the forest by the three good fairies. Aurora believes in true love and has never been shy about expressing her hopes and dreams for the future.

Prince Phillip and Aurora fell deeply in love when they first met in the woods.

The good fairies used their magic to soften Maleficent's curse. Then, they raised Aurora as a peasant girl until her sixteenth birthday.

Merida

Headstrong Merida wants to do things her own way and struggles with the social etiquette of being a princess. However, not totally willing to disregard myths of her land, she boldly follows the wisps wherever they appear.

When Merida's mother, Elinor, is turned into a bear and back to human again, she accepts her daughter following her own path.

Merida's brothers Harris, Hubert and Hamish are always ready to stir up some trouble!

Flower Finds

Aurora is strolling through the flowers in the palace gardens. Help her to spot **10** of her animal friends and the **3** good fairies as she walks along.

Now look for the basket of berries!

CC

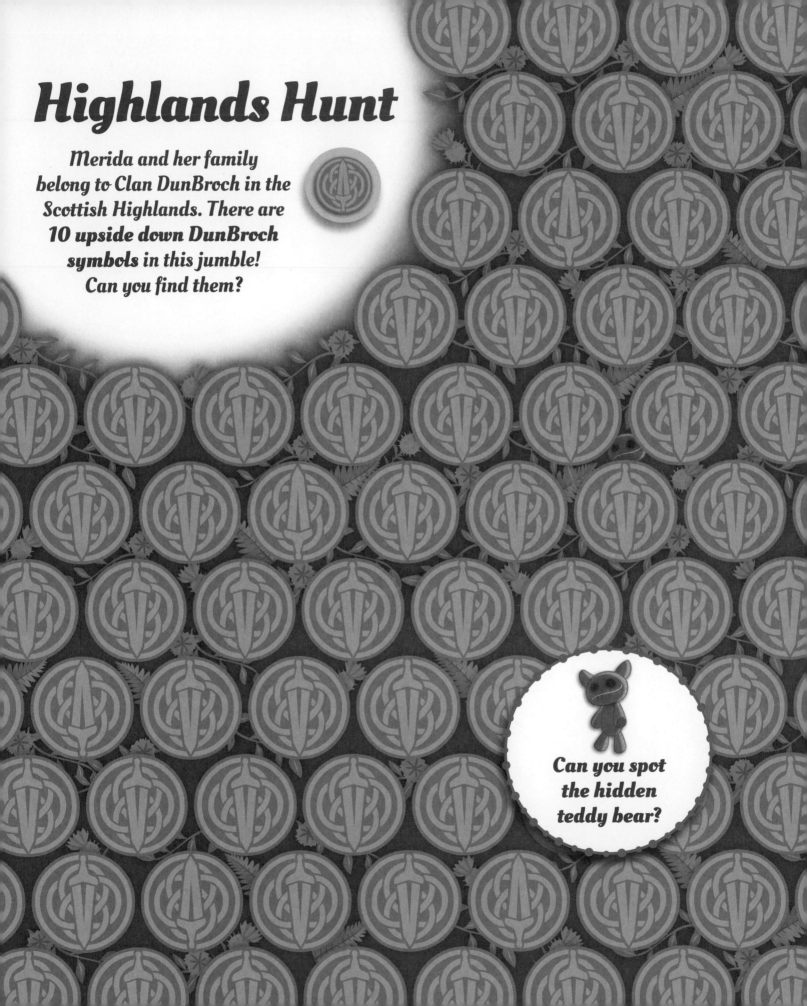

Highlands Hunt

Merida and her family belong to Clan DunBroch in the Scottish Highlands. There are **10 upside down DunBroch symbols** in this jumble! Can you find them?

Can you spot the hidden teddy bear?

Tiana

Tiana always dreamed of opening her own restaurant in New Orleans. Inspired by her father, hard-working Tiana overcame life's obstacles to be successful, having learnt the importance of love along the way.

Charlotte LaBouff has been Tiana's best friend since they were children, and will do anything for her friend.

Jazz fanatic Prince Naveen is visiting New Orleans when he's turned into a frog and meets Tiana.

Snow White

Known as 'the fairest one of all', Snow White is a kind and gentle soul, who makes the best of every situation, no matter how bad. The Prince saves Snow White with True Love's Kiss.

When Snow White flees the Evil Queen, the Seven Dwarfs offer her shelter.

As time goes by, the Dwarfs become protective of Snow White, and will do whatever it takes to keep her safe.

Recipe for Disaster

It's super busy at the restaurant! Tiana needs to find **10 rolling pins** and **5 cups**. Can you help her?

Can you find The Frog Prince on these pages?

Mining Muddle

The Dwarfs have found loads of diamonds in the mine today! There are 10 pickaxes and 7 dwarfs' hats on these pages. Can you help Snow White to find them?

Can you find
the bucket
of gems?

Codebreaker Challenge!

Well done! Now go back through the book and find the pages with the codebreaker challenge badge. Each of these pages has a hidden silhouette, find them all to reveal the hidden message! **CC**

_ _ _ _ _ _ _ _ _ _ _ _ _ _ ,

_ _ _ _ _ _ _ _ _ _ _ _ _ _ !

The Golden Icons Challenge!

Fancy taking on the Golden Icons Challenge? Go back through the book and try to find all of the items below.

x3

x2

x2

x2

x3

x2